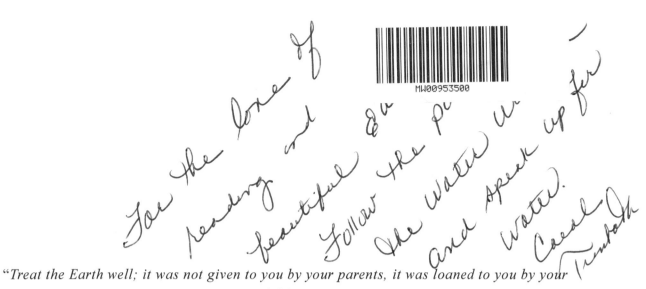

"*Treat the Earth well; it was not given to you by your parents, it was loaned to you by your children.*
We do not inherit the Earth from our Ancestors, we borrow it from our Children."
– Ancient Native American proverb

"*We will be known by the tracks we leave.*"
– Dakota proverb

Acknowledgements

"One finger cannot lift a pebble." – Hopi proverb

"It takes a thousand voices to tell a single story." – Native American proverb

A book is never the solitary work of a writer. One always stands on the shoulders of all who taught, encouraged, and cheered the writer on. My family members were my go-to folks who knew my heart and pushed me forward—Julie and Jon Rosine, Mollie and Jeff Trembath, and Andrea and Brad Trembath. Friends listened countless times to the story, offered insights, created exquisite artwork, and proofread pages, namely: Jeff Stoner, editor; David W. Craig, illustrator; Glendon Haddix, graphic designer; along with Josephine Mandamin, Leslie Helakoski, Joan St. John, Shannon Janeczek, Nancy Frauenheim, Hazel Thompson, Debbie Gonzales, and Linda McLean. Each has touched this book and added to its energy.

Water Walkers

Copyright © 2014 by Carol Trembath

ISBN 13: 978-0-9907446-2-7
ISBN 10: 0-9907446-2-0

Library of Congress Control Number: 2015907005

Illustrations by David W. Craig

Lakeside Publishing

Edited by Jeff Stoner

Printed in the United States of America

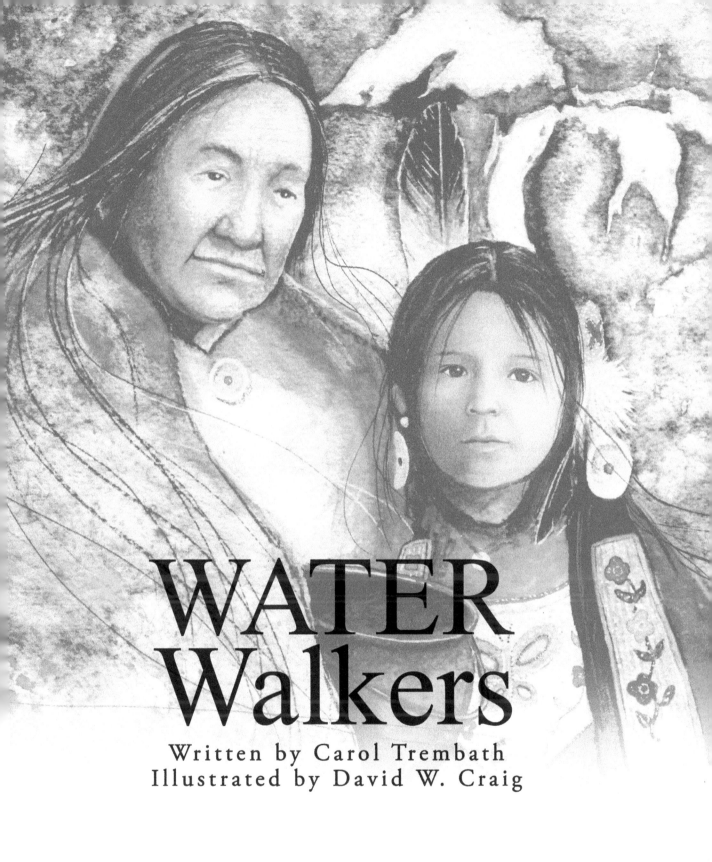

WATER
Walkers

Written by Carol Trembath
Illustrated by David W. Craig

Dedication

THIS BOOK IS DEDICATED TO Grandmother Josephine Mandamin, an Anishinaabe (Ojibway) member and founder of the Mother Earth Water Walkers.

Many years ago Josephine saw that our precious water was in trouble. Water was being polluted and siphoned away. She took up the challenge given to her by the Grand Chief of the Three Fires Midewiwin Lodge when he asked, "What are you going to do about it?"

With the Great Lakes at the heart of the historical Anishinaabe territory, Josephine decided to draw attention to the condition of water by walking the perimeter of each of the Great Lakes. In the spring of 2003, Josephine and a group of supporters began their first water walk by circling Lake Superior. Since then water from lakes, rivers, and even oceans has been carried in copper pails over countless roads in an effort to show others the importance of protecting the water.

Today Josephine's message continues to send out ripples and waves to communities across the Midwest and beyond. There is an ever-widening circle of concerned citizens and civic leaders who are exploring a new vision for water—one that ensures a sustainable future for all of Earth's living inhabitants.

With every step there has been a growing certainty within Josephine regarding her mission, but she felt some concern over my endeavor to write children's books about the Water Walkers story. She shared her uneasiness when she wrote to me, saying:

"I have had misgivings about what you are doing. Many offerings have been made for an answer to my misgivings. In our culture we tell oral teachings or draw. In your culture, it is different. To that I give my respect. I have pondered on the reason why you are doing this. I pondered about ego, money, fame. What is it she wants, I asked? Finally, the response came:

'It is for the Water. Simple—for the water.'

"I give my blessings for the water. Now I can rest easy."

Both Josephine's real life story and Mai's adventure with her grandmother in this book, *Water Walkers*, speak to the heart and soul of this nation. We are all one and part of the Great Circle. Josephine is moving forward to build a deeper awareness of water and of the impact of American culture on the environment.

When asked why she is doing this, she replied, "We are not doing this for ourselves, we're doing this for you. What will you tell your grandchildren when they ask, *what did you do for the water?*"

About the Water Walkers

THE MOTHER EARTH WATER WALKERS, led by Josephine Mandamin, began their journey in 2003 when Native women and men walked 1,300 miles around Lake Superior. In 2004, 2005, 2006, and 2007 the Mother Earth Water Walkers encircled Lake Michigan, Huron, Ontario, and Erie respectfully. In 2008 the Water Walkers revisited Lake Michigan. In 2009 Lake Ontario was circled from Kingston, Ontario to the Atlantic Ocean along the St. Lawrence River. All of the 11,525 miles were walked to call attention to the sacred gift of water.

The Ojibway (Chippewa), Ottawa (Odawa), and Potawatomi are known as the "Council of Three Fires." They are part of a larger group of Native people known as the Anishinaabeg. According to Native tradition, the Ojibway were the caretakers of the Eastern Woodlands and Great Lakes. The Anishinaabe women as givers-of-life were responsible for speaking for, protecting, and carrying the water. Their walk with a copper pail of water was a way of *walking the talk*.

The Mother Earth Water Walkers raised awareness of the need to take care of the water. Walking, the slowest form of transportation, reinforced an ancient value of taking a public stand. Each of the 24,113,700 steps was a prayer for the water, Mother Earth, animals, birds, insects, trees, and the human family.

The animals of the story represent the four directions of the Native Peace Shield: eagle, deer, bear and hare. The central character is Mai. Her name means coyote and coyote is a teacher in Native American folklore. The Ojibway called Lake Superior *Gichigami*—meaning "big water."

The following is a children's fiction story. It is a tribute to the Native women and men who have walked endless miles to draw attention to the condition of water. It is an "imaginary version" that describes what many dedicated and courageous indigenous people have done to protect and preserve water for generations to come. If you would like to learn more about the Mother Earth Water Walkers, go to their website at motherearthwaterwalk.com.

Ka-tink, ka-tink, ka-tink. Water splashed in the copper pail as I walked along the lakeside path.

One step and then another, I tried to keep up with my big sister Winona, Uncle Joe, and my Anishinaabe grandmother.

As I walked I remembered my grandmother's words to her Ojibway people. "Our sacred water is in trouble. We will walk long distances with water in our copper pail and pray for the water with each step. We will circle the lakes to protect them for our children and our grandchildren."

4

Grandmother planned to walk around each of the Great Lakes, one by one. She taught me that it is our Ojibway people's custom to watch over and protect the water. I thought about Grandmother's words. I wondered how I could help.

Grandmother told us we would start the first water walk around the big lake, Gichigami—Lake Superior. I wanted to go too. But my big sister Winona and Uncle Joe said, "Mai, you are too little to go."

My grandmother said, "Even our little ones can make ripples and waves. Mai will tell me what she sees, because she sees like the clever coyote." From then on, I became a Water Walker for Mother Earth.

On a cold and rainy April morning, we began our walk in Odanah, Wisconsin. Uncle Joe carried the eagle staff and I took my favorite doll and held my grandmother's hand.

Each morning before our daily walk, my job was to pour the lake water into the copper pail. Grandmother prayed to bless the water and sang an Ojibway healing song. She took tobacco from her pouch and placed it in the water as a gift of thanks.

After the morning ceremony, we took turns walking. I walked each day with my grandmother. I looked for ways to help because Grandmother told me, "Even little people can do big things."

14

In a busy fishing town, trash floated in the water. Baby ducks swam with empty bottles and cans. One duck was caught in a plastic baggie. Uncle Joe helped me to free it as an eagle circled above me in the sky.

Grandmother said, "You Mai, like an eagle, are developing wings and a keen *sight* to help others. Your vision is increasing." I decided to look for cans and plastic bottles to recycle. I knew I could help!

At sunset, after many miles of walking, Winona and I saw a family of deer. The deer walked a long way over rocks to get a cool drink from the lake. My big sister said, "Deer must now walk much farther out into the lake for their water."

I asked Grandmother, "Where did the water go?"

Grandmother frowned and said, "Our lake water is vanishing, but deer can teach you. Be like the deer and look beyond the water's edge. See what is happening to Mother Earth. Her lifeblood is water. Like the deer, you have a gift to *hear and see* things from a distance." I smiled. Then I remembered Winona telling me to conserve water—to turn it off after I used it. I am helping.

The next day, Uncle Joe pointed out a big bear. We could see the bear splashing in the lake. He was trying to catch a fish. "Too bad he didn't catch anything." My big sister Winona sighed. My grandmother looked worried and whispered to me, "The bear in Indian lore

21

has always been a sign of strength and courage. But today this bear reached far out into the water. He tried to spear a fish with his great claws, but there were none."

Grandmother said, "Are you seeing everything? Bear is asking you to look beneath the water to see something more. There are fewer fish. Like the hibernating bear, go within Mai and seek your answers. But like the sleeping bear, you must also come out of your den. You must *tell others*. This bear is a good teacher."

"But Grandmother," I said, "I am too little to be a teacher. I do not know what to do."

My grandmother pointed out a little rabbit. She spoke softly, "You can learn from the rabbit not to be afraid. Rabbits are known to speak for all the little animals. They do not move forward step-by-step. They make leaps and hops. You can too."

"Rabbits have big families with many brothers and sisters. You have a human family that you can talk with. Tell your family about what is hurting our water and Mother Earth. Talk to your mother and father and everyone who cares about our sacred water. It can begin with you. It is time for more Water Walkers for Mother Earth. Water holds memories. It reflects back to us . . . all of what we *could be, and ought to be.*"

It took us thirty-six days to walk around the big lake—Gichigami. I like being a Water Walker. I will remember how to help Mother Earth—how to conserve water, to pick up trash, and recycle. I will walk with my grandmother again around all of the other Great Lakes.

I can make many more *ripples and waves*. I *know* I can.

Words to Know

Anishinaabe – A member of indigenous people (usually called aboriginal in Canada or First Nations), many of whom live in the U.S. states of Michigan, Wisconsin, and Minnesota, and in Canada in the provinces of Quebec, Ontario, Manitoba, and Saskatchewan.

Biodegradable – Materials that can be broken down by natural processes and absorbed harmlessly into the environment.

Climate change – A measurable change in the climate, temperature, and weather patterns, in the Earth that many scientists believe to be the result of global warming.

Conservation – The protection of animals, plants, and natural resources.

Council of Three Fires – A long-standing Anishinabek alliance of the Ojibway (or Chippewa), Ottawa (or Odawa), and Potawatomi tribes of North America.

Eco-friendly – The label given to actions or items believed to be safe for the environment.

Elders – An older influential member of a family, tribe, or community.

Environment – The conditions that surrounds someone or something that affects its growth, health, and/or progress; the natural world around us.

Fossil fuels – Energy sources such as oil, coal, and natural gas that come from the remains (fossils) of living things from the past. Fossil fuels are burned to produce most of the world's energy.

Four Directions – Native people see the world as having four directions. From the four directions, come the four winds. Each direction has a special meaning and color associated with it.

Global warming – An increase of the average temperature of the Earth's atmosphere that many scientists consider to be the cause of adverse effects such as climate change, melting polar ice caps, decreasing air quality, and rising sea levels.

Greenhouse effect – The process by which gases that accumulate high in the Earth's atmosphere trap heat from the sun, hold it, and bounce it back to Earth. This causes a warming effect upon the Earth's surface, oceans, and atmosphere, similar to what happens inside a garden greenhouse keeping plants warm throughout the winter.

Hibernate – To be in a dormant or inactive state during a cold period, especially during the winter.

Indigenous – Existing, growing, or produced naturally in a particular region or environment.

Landfill – A dumping area, either above or under the ground where large amounts of waste are deposited.

Midewiwin – A society created by Native North American tribes to share and protect the songs, ceremonies, and sacred teachings of and for the Anishinabek people.

Ozone – A form of oxygen high in the atmosphere that protects the Earth from ultraviolet rays of the sun.

Pollution – Harmful or poisonous substances that are released into the air or water supply.

Recycling – The process of reusing materials that would otherwise be thrown away. Recycling saves energy, helps conserve the world's forests, and reduces waste and landfills.

Three sisters – The three main agricultural crops of various Native American groups in North America: winter squash, maize (corn), and climbing beans.

Turtle Island – The Anishinaabe name for the North American continent.

Water cycle – The continuous, natural process by which water evaporates from bodies of water, collects in the atmosphere as vapor, condenses in clouds, falls to the ground as rain, and evaporates again.

Water pollution – The addition of harmful substances such as fertilizers, pesticides, sewage, oil, or toxic waste to natural water.

Cross-Curriculum Activities

Literacy Connections:

- Read: *Brother Eagle Sister Sky*, by Susan Jeffers, Dial, 1991. Ages 5-12.

    - *Compare and contrast this book with* Water Walkers.

- Read: *Dear Children of the Earth,* by Schim Schimmel, Cooper Square Publishing, 1994. Ages 5-10.

    - *Write a letter to Mother Earth telling her what you will do to protect the environment and the animal kingdom.*

    - *Create a postcard to Mother Earth. Depict a clean environment and protected animals. Tell her how you will help keep our earth clean.*

Social Studies and Math Skills:

- Chart the course of the Water Walkers on a map of Michigan and the Great Lakes.

    - *How many miles did they walk? How many footsteps is this?*

        » *Create an illustration of these miles titled "Walk A Mile In My Shoes."*

    - *What sites would the Water Walkers see along the way?*

        » *Create a travel brochure illustrating the above idea.*

    - *Attend a Native American Pow Wow or invite a Native American to your school.*

    - *Learn about, and play, Native American games.*

    - *Listen to Native American music, rhythms, and drumming.*

    - *Learn about the significance of the different forms of music.*

- November is "National American Indian Heritage Month." On a November calendar, list Native American achievements and events.

- Many names of places across North America such as rivers, lakes, mountains and lands came from existing Native American names. How many can you list?

Water Science Activities:

- Research how water is being drained from Michigan's deepest resources and sold by water bottling companies.

- - *Present the pros and cons of this practice.*
  - *Write a persuasive letter to present your viewpoint of this idea.*
- Research water pollution and answer these questions:
  - *Who is polluting our waterways?*
  - *What are some solutions to our water pollution problems?*
  - *When did water pollution become a problem?*
  - *Where does water in your community come from?*
  - *Where does the water go once it is used in your community?*
  - *Why should we protect our water resources?*
  - *How much water is there on Earth?*
  - *Who owns the water?*

Recycling Activities:
- Establish your school as a "Green School."
- Become part of the Paper Retriever program.
- Use recycled materials to create art sculptures and have a "Recycled Art Fair" at your school.

NASA Earth Observatory

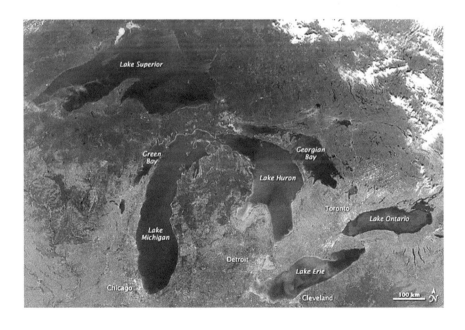

10 Things You Can Do
To Protect the Earth

Save Earth's Natural Resources

The Problem: The human population is growing fast and so are people's demands on the Earth to help us live. The Earth can only reproduce these things so quickly. We need to conserve our natural resources so we do not run out of water, food, and fuel.

1. Save Water. Turn off the faucet while brushing your teeth and you can save up to 1-1½ gallons of water. Taking a shower uses much less energy than filling a bathtub. A shower uses 10-25 gallons of water, while a bathtub uses up to 36 gallons. Even washing your hands and turning off the water as you soap-up, then turning it back on to rinse, is a great way to save water.

2. Save Electricity. Turn off the lights when you leave a room. Remind grown-ups to unplug small equipment like battery chargers for phones and video equipment. They use energy even when they are not plugged into anything. Replace burned-out light bulbs with energy-saving low wattage bulbs. At night, turn off computers.

3. Save Fuel. Heating our homes in the winter and cooling them in the summer, takes lots of energy. Ask parents to raise (in the summer) and lower (in the winter) the thermostat a few degrees. It will save energy and money.

Stop Using Plastic!

Problem: Plastic wraps, containers, and water bottles are polluting our land and water. 90% of plastic bottles are not recycled!

4. Reuse Water Bottles. Fill them with regular tap water.

Reduce, Reuse, Recycle!

The Problem: The human population is increasing and so is the amount of things we use and throw away. Earth can't keep up with all of our garbage. We have to start thinking of ways to reduce, reuse, and recycle.

5. Recycle. Talk to your parents about organizing your family trash. Help your family get into the habit of recycling paper, newspapers, cardboard, plastic bottles, cans, aluminum, and glass containers. Make four labels: Aluminum, Paper, Plastic, and Glass. Tape one sign on each of four home trash containers. Start or participate in a school recycling program too!

6. Reuse. A huge amount of paper and plastic is wasted on shopping bags. Ask parents to buy a few cloth bags that you can always use for shopping.

7. Reduce. Ask your parents to start a compost pile in your backyard to reduce garbage. Fruits, vegetables, scraps, and peelings can all be used to fertilize your garden.

Respect Planet Earth and Slow Down Climate Change

Problem: The increase in the Earth's temperature is causing lots of problems for the environment. Planet Earth gives us everything we need to live a happy life. We need to show planet Earth that we are grateful for all that we have!

8. Trees. Ask your parents or school to plant trees. Trees and plants eat up bad gases. The more trees we have, the cleaner the air.

9. Spend Time in Nature. Instead of watching T.V. or playing indoors, enjoy the fresh air outside and our beautiful planet.

10. Tell a Friend. Share this list with a friend. Everyone can make a difference!

Resources

(K= for Kids; P= for Parents; T= for Teachers)

Websites

Children of the Earth – Promotes a greater understanding and respect for animals, plants, water, soil, air and energy systems. Helps children comprehend the positive and negative environmental effects of our actions. http://www.childrenoftheearth.org/ **K, P, T**

Children of the Seventh Fire – Shows what other students are doing to protect and restore the environment in their communities and create peace. www.childrenoftheseventhfire.com/ **K, P, T**

Environmental Education for Kids – **EEK!** An online magazine for grades four to eight; contains articles and activities about animals, plants, and environmental issues. http://dnr.wi.gov/eek/ **K, T**

EPA: Water Sense Kids – Explores water saving tips for kids at Water Sense! An EPA partnership program. http://www.epa.gov/WaterSense/kids/simpleways.html **K, T**

International Crane Foundation – Works worldwide to conserve cranes and their wetland habitats. https://www.savingcranes.org/ **K, P, T**

Kids for Saving the Earth – Provides an environmental curriculum for all ages that inspires, educates, and empowers children to protect the Earth. www.kidsforsavingearth.org.**K, P, T**

NASA's Climate Kids – Know your world, keep up with the latest, make stuff, play games watch videos, and dream! http://climatekids.nasa.gov/ **K, T**

National Arbor Day – Provides information and resources about planting and caring for trees. www.arborday.org/ **K, P, T**

National Wildlife Federation – Offers fun ways to get kids to experience nature one hour every day! www.greenhour.org **P**

Nature Challenge for Kids – The David Suzuki Foundation website starts with 10 simple ways to protect nature, followed by four challenge activities that offer first-hand experience with the natural world. www.davidsuzuki.org/what-you-can-do/ **K, P, T**

Three Sisters Garden – Provides instruction for planting a Three Sisters Garden. www.kidsgardening.com **K, P, T**

University of Minnesota: An Ojibway Arts in Education Model Program – Combines Ojibway arts and culture with a standard-based curriculum. www.intersectingart.umn.edu **P, T**

Organizations Working to Protect the Great Lakes
(For Parents and Teachers)

Alliance For the Great Lakes – www.greatlakes.org
Clean Water Action Michigan – www.cleanwateraction.org/mi
Great Lakes Echo – www.greatlakesecho.org
Great Lakes Restoration Initiative – www.greatlakesrestoration.us/
Healing Our Waters Coalition – www.healthylakes.org
Sea Grant Michigan – www.miseagrant.umich.edu/
U.S. Environmental Protection Agency (EPA) – www.epa.gov/

Books

Benton-Banai, Edward. *The Mishomis Book: The Voice of the Ojibway.* Hayward: Indian Country Communications, 1998, Print. **K, P, T**

Caduto, Michael J. and Joeseph, Bruchac. *Keepers of the Earth: Native American Stories and Environmental Activities for Children.* Golden: Fulcrum Publishing, 1998, Print. **P, T**

Hart, Lisa. *Children of the Seventh Fire: An Ancient Prophecy for Modern Times.* Granville: The McDonald & Woodward Publishing Company, 2011, Print. **K, P, T**

Jeffers, Susan. *Brother Eagle, Sister Sky: A Message from Chief Seattle.* New York: Dial Books, 1991, Print. **K, P, T**

Kondonassis, Yolanda. *Our House is Round: A Kid's Book about Why Protecting Our Earth Matters.* New York: Skypony Press, 2012, Print. **K, P, T**

Schimmel, Schim. *Dear Children of the Earth: A Letter from Home.* Minnetonka: Cowles Creative Publishing, 1993, Print. **K, P, T**

English Language Arts Standards » Reading Informational Text

Grade 3	
CCSS.ELA-Literacy. RI.3.1	Ask and answer questions to demonstrate understanding of a text, referring explicitly to the text as the basis for the answers.
CCSS.ELA-Literacy. RI.3.3	Describe the relationship between a series of historical events, scientific ideas or concepts, or steps in technical procedures in a text, using language that pertains to time, sequence, and cause/effect.
CCSS.ELA-Literacy. RI.3.7	Use information gained from illustrations (e.g., maps, photographs) and the words in a text to demonstrate understanding of the text (e.g., where, when, why, and how key events occur).
CCSS.ELA-Literacy. RI.3.10	By the end of the year, read and comprehend informational texts, including history/social studies, science, and technical texts, at the high end of the grades 2-3 text complexity band independently and proficiently.
Grade 4	
CCSS.ELA-Literacy. RI.4.1	Refer to details and examples in a text when explaining what the text says explicitly and when drawing inferences from the text.
CCSS.ELA-Literacy. RI.4.3	Explain events, procedures, ideas, or concepts in a historical, scientific, or technical text, including what happened and why, based on specific information in the text.
CCSS.ELA-Literacy. RI.4.10	By the end of year, read and comprehend informational texts, including history/social studies, science, and technical texts, in the grades 4-5 text complexity band proficiently, with scaffolding as needed at the high end of the range.

English Language Arts Standards » Reading Literature

Grade 3	
CCSS.ELA-Literacy. RL.3.2	Describe characters in a story (e.g., their traits, motivations, or feelings) and explain how their actions contribute to the sequence of events.
CCSS.ELA-Literacy. RL.3.3	Explain how specific aspects of a text's illustrations contribute to what is conveyed by the words in a story (e.g., create mood, emphasize aspects of a character or setting).
CCSS.ELA-Literacy. RL.3.10	By the end of the year, read and comprehend literature, including stories, dramas, and poetry, at the high end of the grades 2-3 text complexity band independently and proficiently.
Grade 4	
CCSS.ELA-Literacy. RL.4.3	Describe in depth a character, setting, or event in a story or drama, drawing on specific details in the text (e.g., a character's thoughts, words, or actions).
CCSS.ELA-Literacy. RL.4.9	Compare and contrast the treatment of similar themes and topics (e.g., opposition of good and evil) and patterns of events (e.g., the quest) in stories, myths, and traditional literature from different cultures.
Source: http://www.corestandards.org/	

About the Artist—David W. Craig

David W. Craig

BORN AND RAISED IN THE state of Washington, David W. Craig grew up surrounded by land as alive as it is beautiful. David began private art lessons at the age of nine. After high school graduation, he pursued his life-long passion and earned a degree in art from Seattle Art Institute.

David has done freelance work for national parks and for various commercial organizations, but currently he focuses full time on his own style of painting. Weaving together story, emotion and moments in time with color and a vibrant sensitivity, each of David's pieces speaks to its viewers in a unique and powerful way. Watercolor, mixed media, sculpturing, and leather work are some of his mediums.

Family ties are strong in the foothills of Mount Rainer where David Craig paints and raises his two young daughters on a rural farm. Enrolled Chippewa (Ojibway), David and his daughters travel throughout the western United States attending tribal gatherings, powwows, and art shows.

About the Author —Carol Trembath

Author Carol Trembath (right)
with Josephine Mandamin

BORN AND RAISED IN THE state of Michigan, which is surrounded by the Great Lakes, Carol has made water a lifelong focus and passion.

Her other interest is teaching. Carol has been a teacher, librarian, and media specialist for over 27 years. She earned a Masters Degree in Library and Information Science from Wayne State University and a second Masters in Educational Technology from Michigan State University. However, her initial degree was in English from Western Michigan University and her "first love" is literature.

Her hope is that young readers of *Water Walkers* will become more aware of the Native people's wisdom teachings and also become involved with protecting the environment that Native people love so dearly.

"Water," she said, "is our friend; and if you love something, you take care of it."

Carol has plans for more children's books that will continue Little Mai's journey to all of the Great Lakes. Her next book, titled *Stepping Stones,* will retrace the steps of the ancient Anishinaabeg people as they journeyed westward from the Eastern Woodlands.

Visit her website for more information: CarolTrembath.com

CPSIA information can be obtained
at www.ICGtesting.com
Printed in the USA
BVHW021202060919
557616BV00001B/3/P